Grandma and Grandpa Day

Mc Graw Hill **Wright Group**

The **McGraw·Hill** Companies

"It's Grandma and Grandpa!" Mike said.

Grandpa hugged him.

"That felt like a bear hug," Mike said.

He kissed Grandma.
He **sniffed** her neck.

"Grandma smells like
a rose," Mike said.

"Where is Coco?"
asked Mike.
He didn't see
their cat anywhere.

Mike looked under the sofa.
Mike looked on the bed.
He still didn't see Coco.

"Use your other senses,"
Grandpa said.

"I hear something,"
Mike said.
He heard loud purring.

Mike opened the closet.

"I see something," he said.
He looked down and saw
a tail.

Coco was in the basket.

"I found her!" said Mike.

Grandma smiled and patted
Mike on the back.

Grandpa said it was time
for a snack.

9

Mike took a bite of a muffin.
"This **tastes** great,"
he said.

Grandma ate a muffin too.
Grandpa poured glasses
of milk.

"This is a great Grandma
and Grandpa Day!"
Mike said.

Focus Question

How do I use my five senses?

Sing a song about one of your five senses.

My Home Page